OUR WAY TO...
NEW ZEALAND

The energy behind The FA Cup

The energy behind The FA Cup

TOTTENHAM HOTSPUR
MANCHESTER UNITED
CARDIFF
The energy behind The FA Cup
e·on
TheFA.com

e·on

OKI
SOLUTIONS
27
joma
COMMS
DIRECT

HREIDARSSON
7

THE FA CUP SPONSORED BY E.ON
2008 FINAL
CARDIFF CITY
0
PORTSMOUTH
KANU 37'
1
KRANJCAR (YELLOW) 54'
2008 FINAL

PORTSMOUTH
POMPEY
MARCHING TO
WEMBLEY
POMPEY

e.on
15
TheFA
CUP